2

MARY VISITS ELIZABETH

BLESSED IS THE FRUIT OF THY WOMB. AND WHY DOES THE MOTHER OF MY LORD COME TO ME?

I PRAISE GOD, FOR HE HAS DONE GREAT THINGS TO ME. ALL NATIONS WILL CALL ME BLESSED!

③

AT THE END OF MARY'S VISIT, A SON IS BORN TO ELIZABETH AND ZACHARY.

HIS NAME WILL BE JOHN.

THIS CHILD WILL BE A PROPHET AND WILL GO BEFORE THE LORD TO PREPARE HIS WAYS.

④

NOW WHEN MARY WAS BETROTHED TO JOSEPH, SHE WAS WITH CHILD BY THE HOLY SPIRIT. JOSEPH, BEING A JUST MAN, DID NOT WANT TO EXPOSE HER TO SHAME, SO THOUGHT OF SEPARATING FROM HER PRIVATELY. BUT WHILE HE SLEPT—

FEAR NOT, JOSEPH. THE CHILD TO BE BORN OF MARY IS BY THE HOLY SPIRIT. HE WILL SAVE HIS PEOPLE FROM SIN.

⑤

THUS IT CAME ABOUT AS ISAIAS HAD FORETOLD—"BEHOLD THE VIRGIN WILL BEAR A SON AND THEY WILL CALL HIS NAME 'EMMANUEL' WHICH MEANS GOD WITH US.'"

CAESAR AUGUSTUS HAVING ORDERED A CENSUS, MARY AND JOSEPH WENT TO BETHLEHEM TO BE ENROLLED

THE TOWN WILL BE CROWDED, BUT GOD WILL PROVIDE.

⑥

IS THERE NO ROOM, JOSEPH?

NO! BUT I KNOW OF A STABLE. LET US GO THERE

⑦

THERE, IN A STABLE, JESUS IS BORN AND LAID IN A MANGER.

AND AN ANGEL APPEARS TO SHEPHERDS KEEPING NIGHT WATCH OVER THEIR FLOCKS

I BRING YOU GOOD NEWS! TODAY IN BETHLEHEM IS BORN A SAVIOUR. AND THIS WILL BE A SIGN TO YOU— AN INFANT LYING IN A MANGER

A HOST OF ANGELS APPEAR AND SING.

GLORY TO GOD IN THE HIGHEST. AND ON EARTH PEACE TO MEN OF GOOD WILL!

AFTER THE ANGELS HAVE GONE—

LET US GO TO BETHLEHEM!

YES, AND SEE WHAT THE LORD HAS MADE KNOWN TO US!

AND THEY UNDERSTOOD WHAT HAD BEEN TOLD THEM ABOUT THIS CHILD.

WHEN EIGHT DAYS WERE FULFILLED FOR HIS CIRCUMCISION, HIS NAME WAS CALLED JESUS, THE NAME GIVEN HIM BY THE ANGEL BEFORE HE WAS CONCEIVED IN THE WOMB

JESUS IS BROUGHT TO THE TEMPLE TO BE PRESENTED TO THE LORD ⑬

SIMEON GREETS MARY AND JOSEPH

THIS CHILD IS DESTINED FOR THE RISE AND FALL OF MANY, AND A SWORD OF SORROW SHALL PIERCE YOUR SOUL.

⑭

SOME TIME LATER THREE WISE MEN FROM THE EAST COME TO JERUSALEM.

WHERE IS THE NEWBORN KING OF THE JEWS?

WE HAVE SEEN HIS STAR IN THE EAST AND HAVE COME TO WORSHIP HIM.

⑮

THE KING'S SPIES LEARN OF THE WISE MEN.

WE MUST INFORM HEROD AT ONCE!

⑯

STRANGERS FROM THE EAST ARE SEEKING A NEWBORN KING!

THEY CARRY TREASURE!

SEND THE CHIEF PRIESTS AND SCRIBES TO ME!

⑰

WHERE IS THIS CHILD?

IN BETHLEHEM.

HIS BIRTH WAS FORETOLD BY THE PROPHET MICHEAS!

⑱

HEROD SUMMONS THE WISE MEN. GO TO BETHLEHEM AND BRING ME WORD OF THE CHILD THAT I MAY GO TO WORSHIP HIM.

HA, HA, FOOLISH WISE MEN! I SHALL KILL THIS NEW KING AFTER THEY FIND HIM.

LOOK! THE STAR! IT WILL GUIDE US TO THE CHILD!

WE OFFER YOU GIFTS—GOLD, INCENSE, MYRRH!

WARNED AGAINST HEROD IN A DREAM, THE WISE MEN GO HOME ANOTHER WAY.

WHEN HEROD LEARNED HE HAD BEEN TRICKED... KILL EVERY BOY IN BETHLEHEM TWO YEARS OR UNDER!

BUT, FOREWARNED BY AN ANGEL, JOSEPH FLED WITH MARY AND JESUS INTO EGYPT.

GUESS NOBODY LIVES IN THIS HOUSE!

26

AFTER A YEAR OR TWO.
I WONDER WHEN WE SHALL RETURN TO OUR OWN PEOPLE?

PERHAPS SOON NOW, JOSEPH.

27

ONE NIGHT WHILE THEY SLEPT...

ARISE, TAKE THE CHILD AND HIS MOTHER AND GO INTO GALILEE. HEROD IS DEAD.

28

SO THE HOLY FAMILY SETTLE IN THE TOWN OF NAZARETH IN GALILEE.

IT IS MARY AND JOSEPH!

29

AS YEARS PASS, JESUS GROWS INTO A STRONG AND HELPFUL SON.

30

AFTER HIS TWELFTH BIRTHDAY, JESUS GOES TO JERUSALEM WITH HIS PARENTS FOR PASSOVER.

WHAT A BEAUTIFUL TEMPLE!

31

IN THE TEMPLE JESUS QUESTIONS THE TEACHERS.

AND HOW DO YOU EXPLAIN THIS PROPHECY?

NEXT DAY MARY AND JOSEPH JOIN THE CARAVAN TO RETURN HOME. LATER...

WHERE IS JESUS? HE IS NOT WITH OUR FRIENDS!

THEY HURRY BACK TO JERUSALEM.

HAVE YOU SEEN A LAD OF TWELVE NAMED JESUS?

AFTER THREE DAYS OF SEARCHING...

SON, WE HAVE SOUGHT YOU SORROWING!

DID YOU NOT KNOW I MUST BE ABOUT MY FATHER'S BUSINESS?

AND HE WENT TO NAZARETH WITH THEM AND WAS OBEDIENT TO THEM.

DO YOU UNDERSTAND WHAT JESUS SAID IN THE TEMPLE?

NO, MARY, I DO NOT UNDERSTAND.

AND JESUS ADVANCED IN WISDOM AND GRACE BEFORE GOD AND MAN.

ONE DAY JOHN, SON OF ZACHARY, BEGAN TO PREACH AND BAPTIZE AT THE RIVER JORDAN.

THE PHARISEES ARE BOTHERED BY JOHN'S PREACHING.

DO PENANCE, FOR THE KINGDOM OF GOD IS AT HAND!

WHO IS THIS TROUBLE-MAKER?

JESUS COMES TO JOHN TO BE BAPTIZED.

YOU SHOULD BAPTIZE ME!

LET IT BE THIS WAY NOW.

THIS IS MY BELOVED SON IN WHOM I AM WELL PLEASED!

LED BY THE SPIRIT INTO THE DESERT, JESUS FASTS FORTY DAYS AND IS TEMPTED BY THE DEVIL.

SATAN APPEALS TO JESUS' HUNGER.

IF YOU ARE THE SON OF GOD, CHANGE THESE STONES TO BREAD!

IT IS WRITTEN— MAN DOES NOT LIVE BY BREAD ALONE!

HAVING CARRIED JESUS TO THE TEMPLE TOP, SATAN TEMPTS HIM TO PRIDE.

CAST YOURSELF DOWN! THE ANGELS WILL SAVE YOU!

IT IS WRITTEN— TEMPT NOT THE LORD THY GOD!

FINALLY, SATAN ASKS JESUS TO ADORE HIM.

I WILL GIVE YOU THE WHOLE WORLD IF YOU WILL WORSHIP ME!

BEGONE, SATAN! FOR IT IS WRITTEN— YOU SHALL ADORE AND SERVE ONLY GOD!

46

THEN SATAN LEFT HIM FOR A TIME AND ANGELS MINISTERED TO HIM.

47

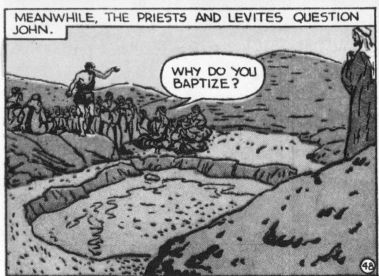

MEANWHILE, THE PRIESTS AND LEVITES QUESTION JOHN.

WHY DO YOU BAPTIZE?

48

ONE MIGHTIER THAN I IS COMING WHO WILL BAPTIZE YOU WITH THE HOLY SPIRIT.

49

JOHN GIVES PUBLIC WITNESS TO CHRIST.

BEHOLD THE LAMB OF GOD!

50

JOHN AND ANDREW, FOLLOWERS OF JOHN THE BAPTIST, DECIDE TO FOLLOW JESUS.

12

JESUS AND HIS FOLLOWERS GO TO GALILEE WHERE THEY ATTEND A MARRIAGE FEAST IN CANA.

JESUS, THEY HAVE RUN OUT OF WINE.

56

JESUS HONORS HIS MOTHER.

FILL THESE JARS WITH WATER; THEN DRAW OUT AND TAKE TO THE STEWARD.

57

WHAT WILL THE STEWARD SAY WHEN WE BRING HIM NOTHING BUT WATER?

LOOK! IT HAS TURNED TO WINE!

58

THE STEWARD WAS SURPRISED AT THE FINE FLAVOR OF THE MIRACULOUS WINE.

HOW IS IT THAT THE BRIDEGROOM HAS SAVED HIS BEST WINE FOR THE LAST?

HE DOESN'T KNOW!

59

THAT WINE WAS MADE FROM WATER!

IT IS A MIRACLE!

60

AND HIS DISCIPLES BELIEVED IN HIM.

JESUS AND HIS DISCIPLES COME TO JERUSALEM FOR THE PASSOVER FEAST.

ANIMALS FOR SACRIFICE ARE BEING SOLD IN THE TEMPLE.

A SCANDALOUS BUSINESS!

WITH ANGER, JESUS CLEARS THE TEMPLE.

DO NOT MAKE MY FATHER'S HOUSE A HOUSE OF BUSINESS!

WHO IS THIS?

THE JEWS CHALLENGE CHRIST.

SHOW US A SIGN OF YOUR AUTHORITY TO DO THESE THINGS.

DESTROY THIS TEMPLE AND IN THREE DAYS I WILL RAISE IT UP!

THEY DO NOT UNDERSTAND THAT CHRIST SPEAKS OF HIS BODY...

IT TOOK 46 YEARS TO BUILD THIS TEMPLE; HOW COULD YOU RESTORE IT IN THREE DAYS?

BUT HIS DISCIPLES REMEMBERED THIS PROPHECY AFTER JESUS HAD RISEN FROM THE GRAVE.

NICODEMUS, A RULER OF THE JEWS, VISITS JESUS AT NIGHT.

THE PHARISEE WANTS TO KNOW IF JESUS IS THE MESSIAS.

MASTER, WE KNOW BY YOUR MIRACLES THAT YOU ARE A TEACHER FROM GOD.

UNLESS A MAN BE BORN AGAIN HE CANNOT SEE THE KINGDOM OF GOD.

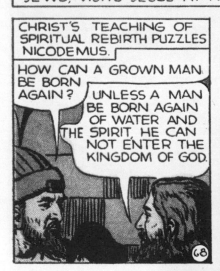

CHRIST'S TEACHING OF SPIRITUAL REBIRTH PUZZLES NICODEMUS.

HOW CAN A GROWN MAN BE BORN AGAIN?

UNLESS A MAN BE BORN AGAIN OF WATER AND THE SPIRIT, HE CAN NOT ENTER THE KINGDOM OF GOD.

THEN JESUS FORETELLS HIS SAVING DEATH ON THE CROSS.

AS MOSES LIFTED UP THE SERPENT IN THE DESERT, SO MUST THE **SON OF MAN** BE LIFTED UP TO SAVE THOSE WHO BELIEVE IN HIM.

BECAUSE THE PHARISEES ARE AROUSED BY HIS WORKS, JESUS AND HIS DISCIPLES LEAVE JUDEA FOR GALILEE. NEAR SICHAR, A TOWN OF THE UNFRIENDLY SAMARITANS, JESUS RESTS AT JACOB'S WELL.

SOMEONE GO INTO TOWN FOR FOOD.

IT WILL BE SAFER IF WE ALL GO.

A WOMAN STARTS TO DRAW WATER.

GIVE ME A DRINK.

71

JESUS DISREGARDS THE USUAL UNFRIENDLINESS BETWEEN JEWS AND SAMARITANS.

WHY DO YOU, A JEW, ASK FOR A DRINK FROM ME, A SAMARITAN?

IF YOU KNEW WHO I AM, PERHAPS YOU WOULD ASK ME AND I WOULD GIVE YOU LIVING WATER.

72

CHRIST IS THE SOURCE OF EVERLASTING LIFE.

HOW CAN YOU GIVE ME LIVING WATER?

THE WATER I WILL GIVE BECOMES A FOUNTAIN OF WATER INTO LIFE EVERLASTING.

73

THEN JESUS REVEALS THE WOMAN'S OWN THOUGHTS.

SIR, I SEE THAT YOU ARE A PROPHET.

I AM THE MESSIAS.

74

SHE HURRIES TO TELL THE TOWNSFOLK ABOUT JESUS.

MASTER, EAT.

MY FOOD IS TO DO THE WILL OF HIM WHO SENT ME.

75

JESUS WINS THEM OVER

WE BELIEVE THAT YOU ARE THE SAVIOR OF THE WORLD.

COME, STAY WITH US.

76

AND HE STAYED WITH THEM TWO DAYS.

AT CANA AN OFFICIAL FROM CAPHARNAUM SEEKS JESUS' HELP

SIR, COME DOWN BEFORE MY CHILD DIES

YOUR SON LIVES, GO YOUR WAY.

77

AT JESUS' WORD, THE CHILD AT CAPHARNAUM IS CURED.

MOTHER!

78

THE OFFICIAL FINDS HIS FAITH HAS BEEN REWARDED

THE FEVER HAS LEFT YOUR SON!

AT WHAT HOUR?

YESTERDAY AT FOUR O'CLOCK.

79

HE WAS CURED WHEN JESUS SAID TO ME, "YOUR SON LIVES."

80

AND HIS WHOLE FAMILY BELIEVED IN JESUS.

JESUS PREACHES TO THE PEOPLE

BE SORRY FOR YOUR SINS THE KINGDOM OF HEAVEN IS AT HAND.

81

THUS WAS FULFILLED WHAT ISAIAS THE PROPHET FORETOLD: "THE PEOPLE WHO SAT IN DARKNESS HAVE SEEN A GREAT LIGHT."

JESUS PREACHES FROM PETER'S BOAT

THAT EVENING CHRIST CURES MANY SICK: AT PETER'S HOUSE.

YOU ARE THE SON OF GOD

EARLY NEXT MORNING PETER FINDS JESUS PRAYING.

THE PEOPLE SEEK YOU

LET US GO INTO NEIGHBORING TOWNS THAT I MAY PREACH THERE ALSO.

NEAR A TOWN THEY ARE STOPPED BY A LEPER.

LORD, IF YOU WILL, YOU CAN MAKE ME CLEAN.

MOVED BY PITY, CHRIST WORKS A MIRACLE

I WILL. I MAKE YOU CLEAN.

BACK IN CAPHARNAUM THE PEOPLE CROWD INTO PETER'S HOUSE TO HEAR JESUS PREACH. JUST THEN...

LOOK! THEY LOWERED THAT PARALYZED MAN THROUGH THE ROOF!

TAKE COURAGE, SON, YOUR SINS ARE FORGIVEN.

THAT IS BLASPHEMY!

WHO CAN FORGIVE SINS BUT GOD ALONE?

JESUS WORKS A MIRACLE TO PROVE HIS POWER TO FORGIVE SINS

ARISE, TAKE YOUR BED, AND GO TO YOUR HOUSE

NEVER HAVE WE SEEN SUCH WONDERS!

MATTHEW, A TAX-GATHERER, IS CALLED TO BE A DISCIPLE.

FOLLOW ME.

MATTHEW'S BANQUET IN THANKSGIVING TO JESUS IS CRITICIZED BY THE PHARISEES.

WHY DOES YOUR MASTER MIX WITH GRAFTERS AND SINNERS?

JESUS HEARS, AND ANSWERS THE COMPLAINTS HIMSELF.

THOSE WHO ARE WELL DO NOT NEED A DOCTOR, BUT THOSE WHO ARE SICK. I CAME TO SAVE SINNERS - NOT SAINTS.

IN JERUSALEM AN ANGEL TOUCHED THE POOL OF BETHSAIDA AT TIMES — AFTER THAT THE FIRST PERSON IN THE WATER WAS CURED.

JESUS CURES A MAN CRIPPLED FOR THIRTY-EIGHT YEARS.

DO YOU WANT TO GET WELL?

SIR, I HAVE NO ONE TO PUT ME IN THE POOL BEFORE THE OTHERS.

TAKE UP YOUR BED AND WALK.

YOU OUGHT NOT TO CARRY YOUR BED ON THE SABBATH.

HE WHO CURED ME SAID, "TAKE UP YOUR BED AND WALK."

WHO ORDERED YOU TO TAKE UP YOUR BED?

HE SLIPPED AWAY.

THE CURED MAN FINDS JESUS IN THE TEMPLE.

SIN NO MORE OR SOMETHING WORSE MAY HAPPEN TO YOU.

THEN THE MAN TOLD THE JEWS OF JESUS' CURE

JESUS ANSWERS THE ACCUSING PHARISEES.

MY FATHER WORKS AND I WORK.

YOU MAKE YOURSELF EQUAL TO GOD.

YOU BREAK THE SABBATH.

HE APPEALS TO HIS MIRACLES.

THE WORKS I DO PROVE THAT THE FATHER HAS SENT ME.

JESUS DEFENDS HIS DISCIPLES.

YOUR DISCIPLES BREAK THE SABBATH BY PICKING GRAIN.

BUT KING DAVID ACTED AGAINST THE LAW BY EATING THE TEMPLE BREAD WHEN HUNGRY.

HE MAKES HIMSELF EQUAL TO DAVID.

AND LORD OF THE SABBATH.

JESUS AGAIN OVERRULES THE PHARISEES.

IS IT LAWFUL TO CURE ON THE SABBATH?

STRETCH FORTH YOUR HAND.

AND THE WITHERED HAND WAS MADE WHOLE.

22

JESUS GOES TO CAPHARNAUM.

111

IN THE CITY A ROMAN OFFICER COMES TO HIM

LORD, MY SERVANT AT HOME IS SERIOUSLY ILL.

I WILL GO AND HEAL HIM

112

LORD, I AM NOT WORTHY TO HAVE YOU ENTER MY HOUSE. SAY ONLY THE WORD AND MY SERVANT SHALL BE CURED

I HAVE NOT FOUND SUCH GREAT FAITH AMONG THE JEWS AS YOU BELIEVE, SO BE IT DONE TO YOU.

AND AT JESUS' WORD THE SERVANT WAS HEALED.

113

THEN, NEAR THE TOWN OF NAIM...

YOUNG MAN, ARISE

114

MY SON!

HE EVEN RAISES THE DEAD!

115

JOHN THE BAPTIST IMPRISONED BY KING HEROD SENDS TWO DISCIPLES TO QUESTION JESUS

(116)

ARE YOU **HE** WHO IS TO COME?

TELL JOHN THE SICK ARE CURED, THE DEAD RISE - AND THE POOR HAVE THE GOSPEL PREACHED TO THEM

(117)

THEN JESUS PRAISES JOHN.

THERE IS NOT A GREATER PROPHET THAN JOHN THE BAPTIST

(118)

AT THE HOUSE OF SIMON THE PHARISEE, A PENITENT ANOINTS JESUS' FEET.

A REAL PROPHET WOULD SURELY KNOW THIS WOMAN IS A SINNER!

(119)

JESUS KNOWS SIMON'S THOUGHTS

IF A MONEY-LENDER CANCELED TWO DEBTS - ONE FOR 500 PENCE AND ONE FOR 50 - WHICH DEBTOR WOULD LOVE HIM MORE?

THE ONE WHO OWED MORE, OF COURSE.

(120)

THIS WOMAN'S MANY SINS ARE FORGIVEN BECAUSE SHE LOVES MUCH

WHO IS HE TO FORGIVE SINS?

(121)

AFTER A TEACHING TOUR, JESUS FREES A BLIND AND DUMB MAN FROM A DEVIL.

CHRIST CONDEMNS THE PHARISEES

ONE EVENING...

LET US CROSS THE LAKE.

127

A STORM AROSE...

128

WAKE HIM!

HURRY OR IT WILL BE TOO LATE!

MASTER WE PERISH!

129

JESUS COMMANDS THE WIND AND WAVES.

PEACE BE STILL!

130

AND THEY WERE FULL OF WONDER AND FEAR BECAUSE THE WIND AND WAVES OBEYED HIM.

AS THE BOAT PUTS ASHORE NEAR GERASA, A DEMONIAC COMES TOWARD JESUS.

WHAT HAVE WE TO DO WITH YOU, JESUS, SON OF GOD?

131

WHAT IS YOUR NAME?

LEGION! THERE ARE MANY OF US.

132

DO NOT SEND US BACK TO HELL; LET US ENTER THE PIGS.

133

LOOK, OUR PIGS ARE DROWNING THEMSELVES!

134

WHEN THE TOWNSFOLK HEAR ABOUT THE LOST PIGS...

GO AWAY FROM HERE!

TAKE ME WITH YOU!

NO: STAY AND TELL EVERYBODY WHAT GOD HAS DONE FOR YOU.

135

AS JESUS APPROACHES CAPHARNAUM, JAIRUS, RULER OF THE SYNAGOGUE, COMES TO HIM FOR HELP.

THOSE WHO WITNESSED THE MIRACLE, QUICKLY SPREAD THE NEWS FAR AND WIDE

JESUS PREACHES IN HIS HOME TOWN, NAZARETH.

THE LORD HAS ANNOINTED ME TO FREE THE CAPTIVES.

TODAY ISAIAS' WORDS ARE FULFILLED!

ANGER SEIZES THE TOWNSMEN.

WHO DOES THAT CARPENTER THINK HE IS?

LET'S GET HIM!

HE ESCAPES.

A PROPHET IS NOT HONORED IN HIS OWN COUNTRY.

AND HE WORKED FEW MIRACLES THERE BECAUSE OF THEIR UNBELIEF.

MEANWHILE, HEROD IS ENTERTAINED BY HIS WIFE'S DAUGHTER, SALOME

A FASCINATING DANCE!

I WILL GIVE YOU WHATEVER YOU ASK!

HERODIAS, WHO HATED JOHN THE BAPTIST FOR CRITICIZING HER, NOW SEIZES HER CHANCE FOR REVENGE.

SHOULD I ASK FOR HALF THE KINGDOM?

NO. ASK FOR THE HEAD OF JOHN THE BAPTIST!

THIS IS A TERRIBLE DEMAND! BUT I MUST KEEP MY PROMISE.

JOHN'S DISCIPLES BURY HIM WITH HONOR.

AFTER THIS MIRACLE, THE PEOPLE WANTED TO MAKE CHRIST KING, BUT HE SENT THEM AWAY AND TOLD HIS APOSTLES TO CROSS THE LAKE TO BETHSAIDA WITHOUT HIM

WHEN THEY LANDED, PEOPLE BROUGHT THEIR SICK TO JESUS TO BE HEALED.

THOSE FED BY JESUS SEEK HIM AT CAPHARNAUM.

IN THE SYNAGOGUE...

WORK FOR THE TRUE FOOD FROM HEAVEN.

WHAT FOOD?

I AM THE BREAD OF LIFE.

IMPOSSIBLE! HE DID NOT COME FROM HEAVEN.

HE WHO EATS MY FLESH AND DRINKS MY BLOOD HAS EVERLASTING LIFE.

CAN ANYONE BELIEVE THAT?

PETER ANSWERS FOR THE TWELVE.

WILL YOU ALSO LEAVE?

NO, LORD. WE BELIEVE YOU ARE THE CHRIST, THE SON OF GOD.

JESUS STAYED IN GALILEE TO ESCAPE THE JEWS WHO WANTED TO KILL HIM.

YOUR DISCIPLES BREAK THE LAW BY NOT WASHING.

YOU MAKE LAWS THAT BREAK THE COMMANDMENTS OF GOD.

YOU MADE THE PHARISEES FURIOUS!

THEY ARE BLIND LEADERS.

AT TYRE A PAGAN ASKS JESUS TO CURE HER DAUGHTER.

I WAS SENT ONLY TO THE CHILDREN OF ISRAEL. IT IS NOT FAIR TO GIVE THEIR FOOD TO DOGS.

EVEN DOGS EAT CRUMBS FROM THE MASTER'S TABLE.

JESUS REPAID HER FAITH BY CURING HER DAUGHTER.

MORE MIRACLES ARE WORKED IN GALILEE.

I CAN WALK!

I CAN SEE!

I CAN HEAR!

GLORY TO GOD! I CAN TALK!

FOUR THOUSAND PEOPLE ARE WITH JESUS THREE DAYS.

I WILL NOT SEND THEM AWAY HUNGRY

BUT WE ONLY HAVE SEVEN LOAVES AND A FEW FISH!

169

NOW FEED THE CROWD

170

HE IS FEEDING US AGAIN BY A MIRACLE!

I WAS THERE WHEN HE FED FIVE THOUSAND WITH TWELVE BASKETS LEFT.

171

THIS TIME WE HAVE SEVEN BASKETS LEFT!

172

WHERE TO, LORD?

LET US GO TO MAGEDAN.

173

THEN THEY SAW HE MEANT THE PHARISEES' TEACHING.

JESUS CURES A BLINDMAN.

DON'T SPEAK OF YOUR CURE AROUND TOWN.

179

WHO DO MEN SAY THAT I AM?

JOHN THE BAPTIST, OR ELIAS, OR JEREMIAS.

180

WHO DO YOU SAY I AM?

181

YOU ARE THE CHRIST, THE SON OF GOD.

YOU ARE PETER, THE ROCK. UPON THIS ROCK I WILL BUILD MY CHURCH AND HELL SHALL NOT DESTROY IT.

182

I WILL GIVE YOU THE KEYS OF THE KINGDOM OF HEAVEN. WHATEVER YOU BIND ON EARTH SHALL BE BOUND IN HEAVEN.

THEN JESUS COMMANDED THEM NOT TO REVEAL THAT HE WAS CHRIST, THE MESSIAS.

I SHALL BE CRUCIFIED AND RISE FROM THE DEAD.

NO! NOT YOU, LORD.

JESUS FORETELLS HIS DEATH AND RESURRECTION.

YOU DO NOT MIND THE THINGS OF GOD.

THE MEANING OF THE CROSS.

MY FOLLOWERS MUST DENY THEMSELVES AND TAKE UP THEIR CROSS DAILY.

WHAT CROSS?

THE VALUE OF SUFFERING FOR CHRIST.

IF YOU LOSE YOUR LIFE FOR ME YOU WILL SAVE IT.

THE VALUE OF A SOUL.

WHAT DOES IT PROFIT A MAN IF HE GAIN THE WHOLE WORLD AND LOSE HIS SOUL?

JESUS TAKES PETER, JAMES AND JOHN TO PRAY WITH HIM.

THE TRANSFIGURATION

IT IS MOSES AND ELIAS TALKING ABOUT THE CROSS!

LORD, WE WILL BUILD THREE TABERNACLES HERE

PETER, THINK WHAT YOU'RE SAYING.

THIS IS MY BELOVED SON, HEAR HIM.

TELL THIS TO NO ONE UNTIL I RISE FROM THE DEAD.

WHAT DOES HE MEAN?

THE OTHER APOSTLES ARE IN TROUBLE

MY SON HAS A DEVIL YOUR DISCIPLES CAN'T CAST OUT

ALL THINGS ARE POSSIBLE TO HIM WHO BELIEVES

GO OUT OF HIM.

HE IS DEAD

STAND UP MY CHILD

LORD, WHY DID WE FAIL?

BECAUSE YOUR FAITH IS WEAK

AT THIS TIME JESUS AGAIN FORETOLD HIS BETRAYAL, CRUCIFIXION, AND RESURRECTION.

AT CAPHARNAUM, OFFICIALS DEMAND THE TAX.

PETER, DO KINGS TAX THEIR OWN SONS?

NO, ONLY STRANGERS.

198

BUT WE'LL PAY, TO AVOID A BAD EXAMPLE. GO, HOOK A FISH.

199

THE COIN IS IN ITS MOUTH. NOW YOU CAN PAY THE TAX.

200

CHRIST SETTLES AN ARGUMENT ABOUT HONOR.

HE WHO DESIRES FIRST PLACE SHALL HAVE LAST.

201

THOSE WHO ARE HUMBLE AS THIS CHILD, ARE GREAT IN MY KINGDOM.

202

WOE TO HIM WHO GIVES BAD EXAMPLE!

203

CORRECT YOUR OFFENDING BROTHER PRIVATELY; THEN, IF NEED BE, TELL THE CHURCH.

SHOULD I FORGIVE MY BROTHER SEVEN TIMES?

204

NO, PETER, SEVENTY TIMES SEVEN.

205

A SCRIBE SEEKS JESUS.

I WILL FOLLOW YOU ANYWHERE.

THE FOXES HAVE DENS AND THE BIRDS HAVE NESTS, BUT THE **SON OF MAN** HAS NO WHERE TO LAY HIS HEAD.

206

44

SEVENTY-TWO DISCIPLES GO FORTH.

I SEND YOU AS SHEEP AMONG WOLVES. HEAL THE SICK AND PREACH.

WOE TO COROZAIN AND BETHSAIDA! WOE TO CAPHARNAUM! IT SHALL GO DOWN TO HELL!

JESUS THREATENS THE TOWNS THAT REJECTED HIM.

THE SEVENTY-TWO RETURN.

DEVILS OBEYED US IN YOUR NAME.

BE GLAD RATHER BECAUSE YOUR NAMES ARE WRITTEN IN HEAVEN.

COME TO ME ALL WHO LABOR AND I WILL REFRESH YOU

45

JESUS VISITS IN BETHANY

LORD BID MARY HELP SERVE

NO MARTHA MARY HAS CHOSEN THE BETTER PART

215

HE ARRIVES AT JERUSALEM FOR THE FEAST OF TABERNACLES.

216

HOW CAN **HE** TEACH, NEVER HAVING LEARNED?

MY TEACHING IS NOT MINE BUT HIS WHO SENT ME.

217

THE PEOPLE ARE BEING DECEIVED.

GO, SEIZE HIM!

218

From this time on, the ruling parties of the Jews raged more than ever. They made a solid front in their deep hatred for Jesus. In the end, they would bring Him to the Cross. But right now, let us go back and try to understand who these powerful men were and how they happened to get their power.

When Christ lived, Palestine was a small province of the mighty Roman empire. The whole country was only 153 miles long, and at its very widest part, only 93 miles. Its size had nothing to do with its importance. During Christ's public life, He covered the length and breadth of the country on foot with His apostles. He preached to all the people and won followers wherever He went.

To the Roman empire, which covered almost all the known world at that time, Palestine was a continual annoyance. Although many of the larger countries which Rome had conquered caused no trouble at all, little Palestine, on the eastern shore of the Mediterranean, had to be watched unceasingly for the first sign of a revolt.

When Christ was born, the Romans ruled the country through King Herod. This Herod was the same one who had the Holy Innocents murdered in his insane jealousy. But when Herod died, his throne was divided between his three sons by the Romans.

Philip got the land in the southern part of the country. Although Christ traveled into this part of the country, Philip did not have any dealings with Him.

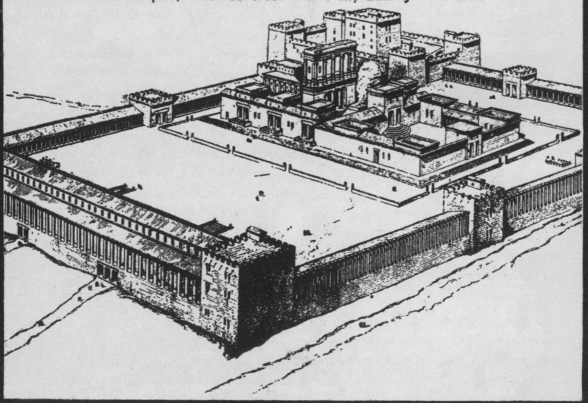

Archelaus, another son, was given the territory in and around Jerusalem. However, the emperor in Rome took this away from him before Christ began His public life because Archelaus could not control the people. Pontius Pilate, a Roman, was later appointed governor of this territory and he was to be the man who sat in judgment on Christ.

Herod Antipas was the only one of the three sons of King Herod who figured in the death of Our Lord. He was ruler of Galilee at the time of the Crucifixion. Since Christ Himself was from Nazareth in Galilee, Pilate sent Him to Herod for judgment. But Herod realized that Christ was accused of a crime which had to be judged by a Roman governor, according to Roman law, so Christ was sent back to Pilate again. Herod and Pilate had originally been enemies, but after this happening, they became friends.

The death of the Saviour took place right outside the walls of Jerusalem. Jerusalem was the capital city of Israel. It was situated in the southern half of the country in the land that had been given to the tribe of Juda after the journey of Jacob's sons from Egypt, a famous story of the Old Testament. The great King David had taken the city from its pagan inhabitants and made it his capital. It has remained the main city of the country ever since.

Since the Jews considered the city their capital, the Romans also governed the province from Jerusalem. Roman soldiers were not allowed to go into the Temple, which was in Jerusalem, but they patrolled all around it keeping a watchful eye on everyone who did go in.

This Temple which plays such an important part in the life of Christ was one of the wonders of the Roman empire. It was not the same Temple that Solomon built, however. The older Temple had been torn down in another invasion of the country, and this new Temple had been built only about thirty years before by King Herod. While Herod was a very bad man, he realized, nevertheless, that he would have to please the Jews in some way to keep them from rebelling against him.

Building that magnificent Temple was his solution to the problem. He spent years gathering the best materials and drawing up plans for the marvelous structure. When it was finished, the Jews were very proud of the building and the Romans were amazed by its beauty.

There was constant friction between the Jews and the Romans. The Jews hated the Romans because they were conquerers. The Jews, of course, were convinced that one day they would gain their independence from Rome and they remembered vengefully every insult they had received. The Romans, on the other hand, did not so much hate the Jews; rather they looked down on them as they did on any conquered people. They just could not understand the intense national pride of the Jews and they did not try to. Naturally, this belittling attitude only increased the hatred of the Jews.

(CONTINUED AT END OF BOOK)

JESUS IS NOW IN JERUSALEM AND HIS PUBLIC LIFE IS DRAWING TO A CLOSE. THE PHARISEES AND THE SADDUCEES, UNITED IN THEIR GREAT HATRED FOR CHRIST, HAVE NOW DECIDED TO KILL HIM AT ALL COST. THEY FIRST TRY TO TRICK HIM WITH CLEVER QUESTIONS, HOPING THAT HE WILL BE FORCED INTO GIVING ANSWERS CONTRADICTORY TO THE LAW. . . .

JESUS IS ATTACKED IN THE TEMPLE.

I AM THE LIGHT OF THE WORLD.

YOUR TESTIMONY IS NOT TRUE.

THE FATHER GIVES TESTIMONY OF ME.

IF YOU DO NOT BELIEVE THAT I AM **HE**, YOU WILL DIE IN YOUR SIN

ABRAHAM IS OUR FATHER

WHOM DO YOU MAKE YOURSELF?

JESUS DECLARES HE IS ETERNAL.

BEFORE ABRAHAM WAS MADE I AM

THEN THEY SEIZED STONES TO HIT HIM BUT HE HID AND LEFT THE TEMPLE.

ON A SABBATH DAY...

GO, WASH IN THE POOL OF SILOE.

THE BLIND MAN WASHED AND WAS CURED.

PHARISEES EXAMINE THE MIRACLE.

WHAT ABOUT HIM WHO CURED YOU?

HE IS A PROPHET.

WE KNOW HE IS A SINNER.

IF HE WERE NOT OF GOD, HE COULD DO NOTHING.

YOU'RE A SINNER. DON'T TRY TO TEACH US.

GET OUT!

JESUS FINDS HIM.

DO YOU BELIEVE IN THE SON OF GOD?

I BELIEVE, LORD.

ARE WE ALSO BLIND?

BECAUSE YOU SAY "WE SEE" YOUR SIN REMAINS.

THEN JESUS LEFT JERUSALEM FOR THE COUNTRYSIDE.

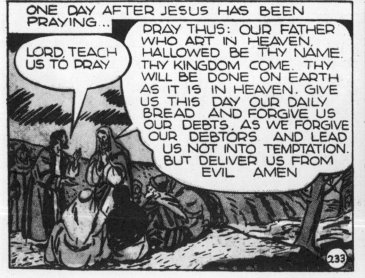

A PHARISEE AND A PUBLICAN PRAYED: THE PHARISEE WAS NOT JUSTIFIED BUT THE PUBLICAN WAS.

THANK GOD I AM NOT A SINNER, LIKE OTHER MEN AND THAT PUBLICAN.

OH GOD, HAVE MERCY ON ME, A SINNER.

WHILE DINING AT A PHARISEE'S...

WHY DIDN'T **HE** WASH?

YOU PHARISEES CLEAN THE OUTSIDE BUT INSIDE YOU ARE EVIL

MASTER, DO YOU ACCUSE US ALSO?

YOU LAWYERS BURDEN THE PEOPLE AND LIFT NOT A FINGER TO HELP THEM

AND THEY MADE PLANS HOW TO ACCUSE HIM.

JESUS TEACHES TRUST IN GOD.

BE NOT ANXIOUS ABOUT FOOD AND CLOTHING GOD FEEDS AND CLOTHES THE BIRDS AND FLOWERS AND YOU ARE WORTH FAR MORE. SEEK FIRST THE KINGDOM OF GOD AND THESE THINGS WILL BE GIVEN YOU.

MASTER, BID MY BROTHER DIVIDE THE INHERITANCE

NO ONE MADE ME DIVIDER OVER YOU

LORD, PILATE KILLED SOME GALILEANS IN THE TEMPLE

UNLESS YOU DO PENANCE, YOU SHALL ALL, LIKEWISE, PERISH

ON A SABBATH IN A SYNAGOGUE...

WOMAN, YOU ARE CURED.

241

COME TO BE CURED ON WEEK DAYS, NOT ON THE SABBATH.

242

JESUS DEFENDS THE PEOPLE.

YOU LOOSEN YOUR OX FOR WATER ON THE SABBATH; OUGHT NOT THIS WOMAN, BOUND EIGHTEEN YEARS, BE LOOSED ON THE SABBATH?

AND THE PEOPLE REJOICED AT WHAT HE HAD DONE

243

LORD, ARE THE SAVED BUT FEW?

STRIVE TO ENTER THE NARROW GATE.

244

BE ON YOUR WAY. HEROD SEEKS TO KILL YOU.

TELL THAT FOX I CAST OUT DEVILS TODAY AND TOMORROW AND THE THIRD DAY I AM CONSUMMATED.

245

58

JESUS ANSWERS A QUESTION OF MARRIAGE.

IS DIVORCE LAWFUL FOR ANY CAUSE?

WHAT GOD HAS JOINED, LET NO MAN SEPARATE

WHY, THEN, DID MOSES ALLOW DIVORCE?

259

BECAUSE OF THE HARDNESS OF YOUR HEARTS; BUT FROM THE BEGINNING, IT WAS NOT ALLOWED.

258

THAT NIGHT THE DISCIPLES RAISE A DIFFICULTY.

IF DIVORCE IS WRONG. IT IS NOT WISE TO MARRY

SOME GIVE UP MARRIAGE FOR THE KINGDOM OF GOD; BUT IT IS NOT FOR EVERYBODY— ONLY FOR THOSE WHO ARE ABLE.

260

IN THE MORNING, THE VILLAGE WOMEN BRING THEIR CHILDREN TO BE BLESSED.

LET THEM COME TO ME.

261

WHOEVER WILL NOT RECEIVE THE KINGDOM OF GOD AS A CHILD, WILL NOT ENTER IT

BEFORE NOON THEY TOOK THE ROAD TO JERICHO.

262

A RICH YOUNG MAN STOPS JESUS ALONG THE WAY.

GOOD MASTER, WHAT SHALL I DO TO HAVE LIFE EVERLASTING?

KEEP THE COMMANDMENTS.

263

WHICH?

YOU KNOW THEM —DO NOT KILL, DO NOT STEAL....

264

I HAVE ALWAYS KEPT THESE. WHAT ELSE?

TO BE PERFECT, GIVE THE POOR YOUR RICHES AND FOLLOW ME, AND YOU SHALL HAVE TREASURE IN HEAVEN.

265

BUT THE YOUNG MAN TURNED AWAY, SAD BECAUSE HE LOVED HIS RICHES

HOW HARD IT IS TO ENTER HEAVEN IF YOU TRUST IN RICHES!

LORD, WE HAVE LEFT ALL. WHAT SHALL BE OUR REWARD?

266

ANYONE WHO LEAVES ALL FOR MY SAKE SHALL RECEIVE A HUNDRED TIMES MORE AND LIFE EVERLASTING.

267

HAVING ARRIVED IN JERUSALEM, JESUS WALKS IN THE TEMPLE.

WHY KEEP US GUESSING? IF YOU ARE THE MESSIAS, TELL US.

THE WORKS I DO IN MY FATHER'S NAME ARE PROOF. I AND THE FATHER ARE ONE.

268

THEY THREATEN HIS LIFE.

FOR WHICH WORK DO YOU STONE ME?

FOR BLASPHEMY; BECAUSE YOU, WHO ARE ONLY MAN, HAVE MADE YOURSELF GOD.

269

ONCE MORE, HE REMINDS THEM OF HIS MIRACLES,

IF I DO NOT THE WORKS OF THE FATHER, BELIEVE NOT

SEIZE HIM!

270

BUT JESUS ESCAPED WITH HIS APOSTLES TO THE JORDAN.

271

64

A MESSENGER FROM BETHANY BRINGS NEWS.

LORD, YOUR FRIEND LAZARUS IS SICK.

THIS SICKNESS IS TO GLORIFY THE SON OF GOD.

272

AFTER A DELAY OF TWO DAYS...

LAZARUS IS DEAD. LET US GO TO JUDEA.

YOUR ENEMIES WILL STONE YOU.

LET US GO AND DIE WITH HIM.

273

AT BETHANY IN JUDEA MARTHA MEETS THE LORD.

YOUR BROTHER LAZARUS SHALL RISE AGAIN.

I KNOW HE SHALL RISE ON THE LAST DAY.

274

JESUS TEACHES THE RESURRECTION.

I AM THE RESURRECTION AND THE LIFE. HE WHO BELIEVES IN ME, THOUGH HE BE DEAD, SHALL LIVE DO YOU BELIEVE THIS?

LORD, I BELIEVE YOU ARE THE CHRIST, THE SON OF THE LIVING GOD.

275

THEN MARTHA CALLED MARY.

THE MASTER IS HERE AND ASKS FOR YOU.

276

65

WHEN THE PHARISEES' SPIES REPORT THE RAISING OF LAZARUS TO LIFE, CAIPHAS DECREES CHRIST'S DEATH.

HE DOES MANY MIRACLES. SOON ALL WILL BELIEVE HIM AND ROME WILL DESTROY US.

ONE MAN MUST DIE TO SAVE THE NATION.

281

CHRIST AGAIN FORETELLS HIS DEATH AS HE DETERMINES TO RETURN TO JERUSALEM.

THE SON OF MAN SHALL BE SCOURGED AND CRUCIFIED, AND ON THE THIRD DAY HE SHALL RISE.

282

ON THE WAY, JAMES AND JOHN ANGER THE OTHERS BY SEEKING HONOR

GIVE US FIRST PLACES IN YOUR KINGDOM.

IT IS NOT MINE, BUT MY FATHER'S, TO GIVE THAT.

283

CHRIST TEACHES A LESSON IN HUMILITY.

LET HIM THAT WILL BE FIRST AMONG YOU BE YOUR SERVANT. BECAUSE THE SON OF MAN IS COME TO SERVE AND TO GIVE HIS LIFE FOR MANY.

284

THAT AFTERNOON THEY REACHED JERICHO. IN THE OFFICE OF ZACHEUS, A TAX-COLLECTOR...

WHAT'S THE PARADE OUTSIDE?

JESUS OF NAZARETH IS PASSING BY!

285

ZACHEUS GETS AHEAD OF THE CROWD.

I MUST SEE HIM!

286

JESUS SALUTES HIM.

ZACHEUS, COME DOWN. TODAY I STAY WITH YOU.

WHAT! HE GOES TO EAT WITH A SINNER.

287

ZACHEUS IS CONVERTED TO JESUS.

LORD, HALF MY GOODS I GIVE TO THE POOR AND FOURFOLD TO THOSE I HAVE CHEATED.

TODAY, SALVATION HAS COME TO THIS HOUSE.

288

NEXT DAY, JESUS CURES TWO BLINDMEN OUTSIDE OF JERICHO.

289

68

NEWS OF JESUS REACHES JERUSALEM.

JESUS OF NAZARETH IS COMING!

295

CROWDS RUSH OUT TO MEET HIM

296

HOSANNAH TO THE SON OF DAVID!

MASTER, REBUKE THEM.

IF THESE ARE SILENT, THE STONES WILL CRY OUT.

297

CHRIST FORETELLS THE DESTRUCTION OF JERUSALEM.

HE IS WEEPING!

O JERUSALEM! BECAUSE YOU KILL THE PROPHETS THERE SHALL NOT REMAIN OF YOU A STONE UPON A STONE.

298

AFTER THIS, THEY WENT ON INTO THE CITY.

THE PEOPLE PROCLAIM CHRIST.

BLESSED IS THE KING WHO COMES IN THE NAME OF THE LORD!

EVERYBODY IS FOLLOWING HIM!

299

JESUS ENTERS THE TEMPLE AND DRIVES OUT THE BUYERS AND SELLERS.

MY HOUSE IS A HOUSE OF PRAYER

300

THEN MANY SICK WERE BROUGHT TO HIM AND HE CURED THEM.

301

NEXT DAY HE TEACHES IN THE TEMPLE.

HAVE FAITH. ALL THINGS THAT YOU ASK IN PRAYER, BELIEVING, YOU SHALL RECEIVE. FORGIVE YOUR BROTHER AND YOUR HEAVENLY FATHER WILL FORGIVE YOU

302

JESUS OUTSMARTS THE PHARISEES WITH A QUESTION.

WHO GAVE YOU THE RIGHT TO TEACH?

WAS JOHN THE BAPTIST FROM GOD OR FROM MEN?

303

THE PHARISEES SEE THEY ARE TRAPPED.

IF WE SAY FROM GOD, HE WILL SAY, "WHY DID YOU NOT BELIEVE HIM?" IF WE SAY FROM MEN, THE PEOPLE WILL ATTACK US.

304

THEY DODGE THE QUESTION.

WE DO NOT KNOW.

THEN NEITHER DO I TELL YOU BY WHAT AUTHORITY I DO THESE THINGS.

305

JOHN PREACHED IN JUSTICE AND YOU DID NOT BELIEVE. THE PUBLICANS WILL ENTER THE KINGDOM OF GOD BEFORE YOU BECAUSE THEY BELIEVED JOHN.

306

THE PHARISEES PLOT TO ACCUSE JESUS OF REBELLION.

APPROVING TAX TO CAESAR WILL ANGER THE PEOPLE; NOT TO APPROVE WILL OFFEND CAESAR.

TRY THE QUESTION ON HIM.

MASTER, WE KNOW YOU TEACH TRUTH. IS TAX TO CAESAR LAWFUL?

DECEIVERS! WHOSE PICTURE IS ON THE COIN?

CAESAR'S.

GIVE CAESAR WHAT IS HIS, AND GIVE GOD WHAT IS GOD'S

THAT SILENCES THEM.

JESUS TRIES TO WIN THEM OVER.

WHOSE SON IS THE CHRIST?

KING DAVID'S.

THEN WHY IN SCRIPTURE DOES DAVID CALL CHRIST HIS LORD?

BUT THE PHARISEES WOULD NOT BELIEVE IN JESUS.

CHRIST WARNS THE PEOPLE AGAINST THEIR LEADERS.

THE SCRIBES AND PHARISEES HAVE AUTHORITY FROM MOSES: DO WHAT THEY SAY, BUT NOT WHAT THEY THEMSELVES DO. THEY BURDEN OTHERS AND CARRY NOTHING; THEY PARADE THEIR WORKS BEFORE MEN AND SEEK FIRST PLACES.

WOE TO YOU, SCRIBES AND PHARISEES, DECEIVERS! YOU SHUT THE KINGDOM OF HEAVEN TO MEN AND DEVOUR THE HOUSES OF WIDOWS; HOW WILL YOU FLEE THE JUDGMENT OF HELL?

MEANWHILE, IN JERUSALEM. JESUS' ENEMIES ARE HAVING TROUBLE.

TO SEIZE HIM ON THE PASCHAL FEAST WILL CAUSE A RIOT.

A FOLLOWER OF JESUS IS AT THE DOOR.

331

THEN THEY BROUGHT JUDAS IN.

WELL?

WHAT WILL YOU PAY IF I LEAD YOU TO HIM?

332

JUDAS LEFT WHEN THEY PROMISED HIM THIRTY SILVER COINS.

NEXT EVENING JESUS BEGINS THE PASCHAL FEAST WITH HIS TWELVE.

I BELONG FIRST

NO. I DO

LET YOUR LEADER BE AS YOUR SERVANT

333

HE WASHES THEIR FEET AS AN EXAMPLE.

NOW YOU ARE CLEAN, BUT NOT ALL.

334

AS THE FEAST GOES ON, JESUS FORETELLS HIS BETRAYAL.

ONE OF YOU WILL BETRAY ME

IS IT I?

IS IT I?

335

LATER...

DO WHAT YOU HAVE IN MIND QUICKLY

336

AND JUDAS WENT OUT INTO THE NIGHT.

JESUS KEEPS HIS PROMISE TO GIVE HIMSELF AS FOOD.

TAKE AND EAT, THIS IS MY BODY.

(337)

DRINK THIS, ALL OF YOU. THIS IS MY BLOOD TO BE SHED FOR YOU FOR THE REMISSION OF SINS. DO THIS IN REMEMBRANCE OF ME.

(338)

HE WARNS OF THEIR DESERTION

TONIGHT YOU SHALL ALL FAIL ME

LORD, I WILL DIE FOR YOU.

(339)

PETER, YOU WILL DENY ME; BUT I HAVE PRAYED THAT YOUR FAITH MAY NOT FAIL, THAT YOU MAY BE CONVERTED AND SUPPORT YOUR BRETHREN.

(340)

JESUS' LAST WORDS WITH HIS APOSTLES.

MEN SHALL KNOW YOU ARE MY DISCIPLES BY YOUR LOVE FOR ONE ANOTHER.

341

I GO TO PREPARE A PLACE FOR YOU.

LORD, WE KNOW NOT WHERE YOU YOU GO, NOR THE WAY.

342

I AM THE WAY, THE TRUTH, AND THE LIFE

343

JESUS PRAYS FOR UNITY AMONG HIS BELIEVERS.

HOLY FATHER, I PRAY THAT THESE AND ALL WHO THROUGH THEM WILL BELIEVE IN ME MAY BE ONE; THAT THE WORLD MAY KNOW YOU HAVE SENT ME.

THEN THEY LEFT THE CHAMBER FOR THE GARDEN OF OLIVES.

344

JESUS TAKES PETER, JAMES AND JOHN INTO THE GARDEN OF OLIVES.

MY SOUL IS SORROWFUL. STAY HERE AND WATCH WHILE I GO TO PRAY.

345

WHILE JESUS PRAYS, THE APOSTLES SLEEP.

FATHER, THY WILL BE DONE.

346

HE WAKES PETER.

WATCH AND PRAY AGAINST TEMPTATION.

347

HE RETURNS AND PRAYS IN AGONY.

THY WILL BE DONE

348

AND HIS SWEAT BECAME AS DROPS OF BLOOD.

HIS ENEMIES REACH THE GARDEN.

LET US GO, THE TRAITOR IS HERE.

SEIZE THE ONE I KISS.

349

WHEN THEY TOOK JESUS, HIS DISCIPLES FLED.

WHILE JESUS IS BEING TAKEN PRISONER, THE HIGH PRIEST MAKES READY THE TRIAL.

CALL THE JUDGES! BRIBE THE WITNESSES.

350

JESUS IS QUESTIONED BUT SAYS NOTHING

THE WITNESSES DISAGREE

351

FINALLY CAIPHAS FORCES CHRIST TO ANSWER.

BY THE LIVING GOD. TELL US IF YOU ARE THE CHRIST, THE SON OF GOD.

I AM AND YOU SHALL SEE THE SON OF MAN COMING IN THE CLOUDS WITH THE POWER OF GOD.

352

YOU HEARD THE BLASPHEMY WHAT DO YOU SAY?

HE IS GUILTY OF DEATH

353

THEN THEY STRUCK AND SPIT ON HIM.

PILATE WILL CONDEMN HIM TOMORROW

354

JUDAS, HEARING THE DEATH SENTENCE, KILLED HIMSELF.

85

AFTER A NIGHT IN PRISON, JESUS IS BROUGHT BEFORE THE ROMAN GOVERNOR.

WHAT IS THE COMPLAINT?

HE MISLEADS THE PEOPLE AND CLAIMS TO BE A KING

359

PILATE QUESTIONS JESUS PRIVATELY.

ARE YOU A KING?

MY KINGDOM IS NOT OF THIS WORLD, OR MY FOLLOWERS WOULD FIGHT FOR ME.

360

MOVED BY JESUS' CHARACTER, PILATE OPPOSES THE PHARISEES.

I FIND HIM FREE FROM GUILT.

HE PREACHES REBELLION HERE AND IN GALILEE.

361

PILATE SENT JESUS TO HEROD, KING OF GALILEE, ABOUT THIS NEW COMPLAINT. BUT HEROD MADE FUN OF JESUS AND SENT HIM BACK, UNCONDEMNED. PILATE THEN OFFERED THE JEWS A CHOICE...

TO HONOR YOUR FEAST, I WILL FREE THE ROBBER BARABBAS. OR JESUS

GIVE US BARABBAS CRUCIFY JESUS.

362

THEN, TO AROUSE THEIR PITY, HE ORDERED JESUS SCOURGED.

88

JESUS CARES FOR HIS MOTHER

JOHN, BEHOLD YOUR MOTHER.

AND JOHN TOOK HER AS HIS OWN.

I THIRST.

WHEN A SOLDIER OFFERED HIM VINEGAR, HE WOULD NOT DRINK.

AT LAST, AFTER THREE HOURS' AGONY...

FATHER, I GIVE MY SOUL INTO YOUR HANDS.

AFTER JESUS DIED THERE WERE EARTHQUAKES, THE TEMPLE VEIL TORE, AND MANY REPENTED.

JESUS' FRIENDS HURRIED HIM TO THE TOMB OF JOSEPH OF ARIMATHEA BECAUSE THE SABBATH BEGAN AT SUNDOWN.

THE PHARISEES ARE STILL WORRIED.

HE'S DEAD I SAW A SOLDIER SPEAR HIS SIDE

BUT HE SAID HE WOULD RISE. SET GUARDS AT THE TOMB TO WATCH THE BODY.

89

EARLY THE THIRD MORNING, CHRIST RETURNS FROM THE DEAD.

371

WOMEN COME TO ANOINT THE BODY.

THE BODY IS GONE! I MUST TELL PETER.

372

THEY MEET AN ANGEL.

HE IS RISEN. GO TELL HIS APOSTLES HE WILL MEET THEM IN GALILEE

373

PETER AND JOHN CAME AND FOUND THE TOMB EMPTY, BUT LATER JESUS APPEARED TO PETER.

THE SAME DAY, JESUS ALSO APPEARED TO MARY MAGDALENE, WHO CAME TO WEEP AT THE TOMB.

MARY

374

MASTER.

GO, TELL MY APOSTLES I ASCEND TO MY FATHER AND YOUR FATHER.

375

THE PHARISEES SPREAD A LIE.

WHAT HAPPENED AT THE TOMB?

LIGHTNING AND AN EARTHQUAKE THEN THE BODY WAS GONE

376

BUT THE PHARISEES PAID THE GUARDS TO SPREAD THE STORY THAT THE APOSTLES STOLE THE BODY.

TWO DISCOURAGED DISCIPLES LEAVING JERUSALEM ARE JOINED BY A STRANGER.

WHY ARE YOU SAD?

HAVEN'T YOU HEARD THE NEWS?

377

WHAT NEWS?

THE CRUCIFIXION OF JESUS, THE PROPHET, IN WHOM WE HAD HOPED

378

THEN THE STRANGER EXPLAINED FROM SCRIPTURE WHY JESUS HAD TO DIE.

OUGHT NOT CHRIST TO SUFFER AND SO ENTER GLORY AS MOSES AND THE PROPHETS FORETOLD?

COME, EAT WITH US.

379

WHEN HE BROKE BREAD THEY KNEW IT WAS JESUS, BUT HE DISAPPEARED.

IN GALILEE, WHILE THE APOSTLES FISH, JESUS APPEARS.

CAST YOUR NET ON THE RIGHT SIDE AND YOU WILL CATCH SOME.

388

THEN THEIR NET WAS FILLED WITH FISH AND THEY KNEW IT WAS JESUS

JESUS WELCOMES THEM ASHORE.

HAVE SOME FOOD.

389

AFTER BREAKFAST JESUS KEEPS HIS PROMISE TO MAKE PETER LEADER.

PETER, DO YOU LOVE ME?

LORD, YOU KNOW THAT I LOVE YOU.

390

FEED MY SHEEP AND LAMBS.

391

CHRIST COMMANDS HIS APOSTLES TO TEACH THE WORLD.

ALL POWER IN HEAVEN AND ON EARTH IS GIVEN TO ME. GO, TEACH ALL NATIONS WHAT I HAVE COMMANDED YOU, BAPTIZING THEM IN THE NAME OF THE FATHER AND OF THE SON AND OF THE HOLY GHOST. HE WHO BELIEVES SHALL BE SAVED. HE WHO DOES NOT SHALL BE CONDEMNED AND I AM WITH YOU TILL THE END OF THE WORLD.

392

JESUS TALKS TO THE DISCIPLES ON MT. OLIVET AND ASCENDS INTO HEAVEN.

YOU SHALL BE WITNESS OF THESE THINGS, BUT STAY IN JERUSALEM UNTIL YOU RECEIVE POWER FROM ON HIGH.

393

THEN HE ROSE INTO THE CLOUDS OUT OF THEIR SIGHT.

The general policy of the Romans toward any of their conquered lands was to allow the inhabitants to keep many of their former customs and laws. Through centuries of experience the Romans had found out that in the long run, conquered people were less unhappy when life continued on much as it was when they were still free.

So it was that the Jews in Jerusalem still had a ruling body of their own which was called the Sanhedrin. This Sanhedrin had a membership of 71 men, all chosen from among the high priests, ancients, and scribes. Before the coming of the Romans, it had been the supreme law-making group of the entire kingdom and there was no court of higher appeal from its judgments. But when the Romans came, they took away some of the power of the Sanhedrin, such as that of passing a death sentence and declaring war. There were smaller Sanhedrins in the smaller Jewish cities and towns, but they all came under the Great Sanhedrin in Jerusalem.

The Pharisees and the Sadducees were the two principal parties of the Jews when Christ lived. As you will recall, both parties were opposed to the teachings of Christ, but that is one of the very few things that these two factions agreed on. Both were very influential at this time, however, and the Sanhedrin was made up almost entirely of members of both parties.

Religious belief was at the bottom of the differences between the two. The Sadducees believed that the Old Testa-

ment, and particularly the first five books of the Old Testament, contained all the law that the Jews had to believe or follow. The Pharisees, on the other hand, taught that there were two elements to the law: the Old Testament and the traditions that had been handed down for centuries.

Naturally, this led to many serious difficulties. The Pharisees kept writing down the ancient traditions and insisting that these writings were binding in conscience on all Jews. The weight of the law, as the Pharisees understood it, grew heavier and heavier upon the people who had to follow it.

By the time of Christ, the law of the Pharisees was so complicated that the people were very confused about it. Many of the minute regulations could not be followed without great hardship. Many times, Christ accused the Pharisees of not following their own law while at the same time they were despising the other Jews who could not follow it. In general, however, Christ did not condemn the law of the Pharisees as much as he did their hypocritical and scandalous lives.

Since the law of the Sadducees was found in the books of the Old Testament for the most part, it was not nearly as difficult to follow. The Sadducees thought the Pharisees were going far beyond the intentions of God when they made laws governing practically every act of man. The disputes between the two parties grew more bitter and heated all the time.

The Scribes were another faction of the Jews, although they were not a party such as the Pharisees and Sadducees. While Scribes did not necessarily belong to either of these two parties, most of them were Pharisees in practise. Scribes were men who made a lifework of studying and interpreting the law. They were highly respected by the Jews because of the great learning they received from their studies.

It is important to know that the Pharisees and the Sadducees both united to crucify Christ. The Pharisees hated Him from the beginning because He showed that some of their interpretations of the law were incorrect. The Pharisees saw plainly enough that if the Jews followed the teachings of Christ, then the pharisaical teachings would soon cease to be important and they themselves would no longer keep their great power.

The Sadducees also hated Christ from the beginning, but for a different reason. They saw that He intended to make certain additions to the Old Testament law and certain changes in their interpretation of it. Like the Pharisees, they recognized that Christ was a threat to their power and prestige.

Both parties knew they would have to get rid of Christ somehow. His Gospel of love was attracting new followers every day. First they tried to trick Him into making statements that would turn the people away from Him. But every time they tried these schemes, Christ saw through their intentions and used the plots to His own advantage. The plots only made the plotters look foolish while Christ was winning more followers. In the end, leaders of the Pharisees and Sadducees realized that Christ had shown their true worth so plainly that they would have to kill Him in order to save their own power. The good men — and there were good men in both parties — were unable to hold them back.

Not much is known of the later life of most of the Jewish and civil authorities connected with the Passion. Both Herod and Pilate fell from power not long afterwards. But there is no record of the death of either man.

Jerusalem was completely destroyed as Christ had prophesied. The great Temple was torn down by the Romans after they had crushed an unsuccessful revolt of the entire Jewish nation. The party of the Sadducees was completely wiped out in this revolt. The Pharisees survived the revolt and became the main party of the Jews, but the Jews themselves became a nation without a home.

But the Man whom the leaders of the Jews thought was the obscure son of the carpenter of Nazareth—whose life and teachings they were sure they had completely wiped out of the pages of history —this Man's kingdom continued to grow and spread till now, when the Name of Jesus is known everywhere in the world. Today His Church still wins the struggle against the forces of evil from its firm position between earth and heaven. There it will stand till the end of time.